Cello

Scales, Arpeggios & Studies

for Trinity College London
exams from 2016

Initial–Grade 8

Published by
Trinity College London Press Ltd
trinitycollege.com

Registered in England
Company no. 09726123

Third impression, November 2018

Printed in England by Caligraving Ltd

Examples of scale and arpeggio bowing patterns

The examples below are given as indications of bowing patterns for all instruments from the syllabus. Clefs, key and time signatures have been deliberately omitted in order not to imply an association with any one scale or member of the string family, or any particular interpretation or emphasis within each scale.

One octave scale, slurred in pairs with a long tonic

or (for Grade 1 only):

Two octave scale, slurred in pairs with a long tonic

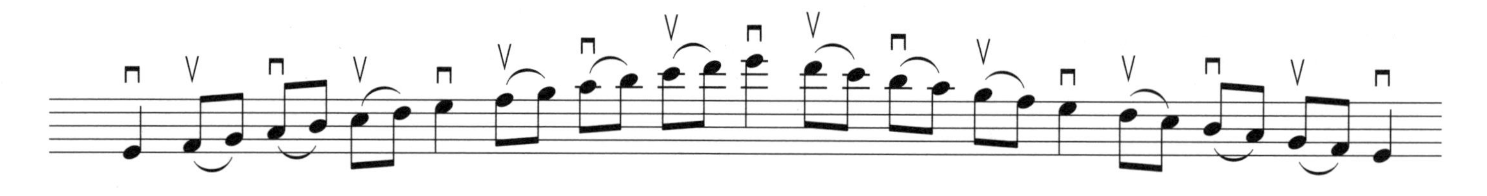

Scale slurred two crotchet beats to a bow

Scale slurred four crotchet beats to a bow

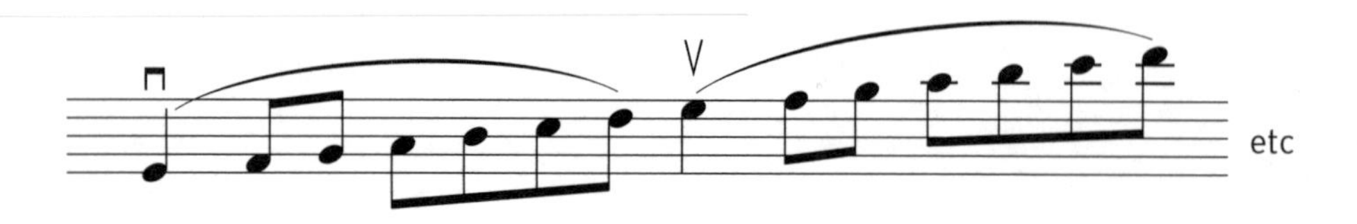

Scale slurred three octaves to a bow (one bow up and one bow down, with a change of bow on the top note)

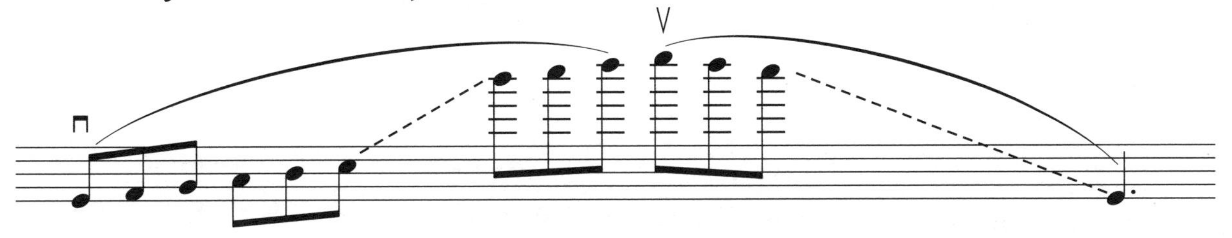

Arpeggio slurred three notes to a bow (one octave)

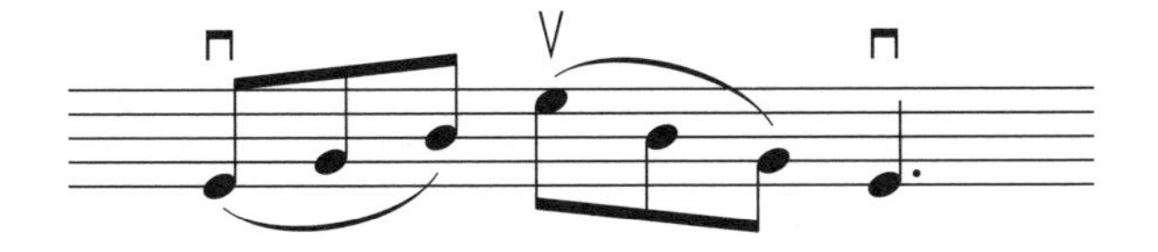

Arpeggio slurred three notes to a bow (two octaves)

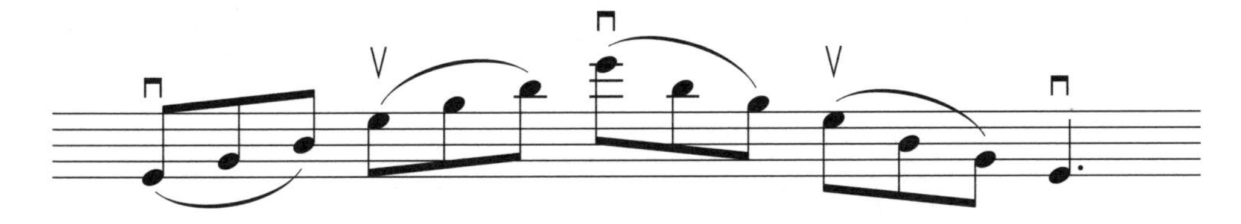

Arpeggio to a 12th slurred three notes to a bow

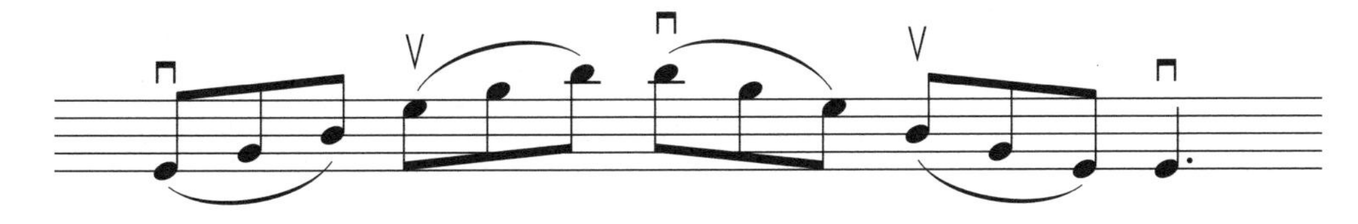

Arpeggio of a 7th slurred in pairs

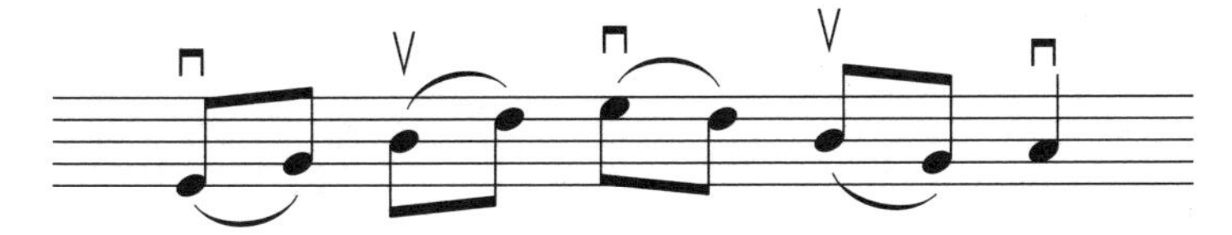

Initial

Scales (all from memory):

The following scales to be performed with the indicated rhythmic patterns on each note (min. ♩ = 88):

C major scale (one octave)

G major scale (one octave)

D major scale (one octave)

Grade 1

<table>
<tr><th colspan="4">Candidates to prepare i) Bowing exercise</th></tr>
<tr><td colspan="4">i) Bowing exercise (from memory):
Candidates should play one of the Grade 1 scales, freely chosen from the list, with two separate crotchets on each degree of the scale, one down bow and one up bow. [♩ = 72]</td></tr>
<tr><th colspan="4">Candidates to prepare in full either section ii) or section iii)</th></tr>
<tr><td colspan="4">either ii) Scales, arpeggios & technical exercise (from memory):
Candidates should play the scale and then the arpeggio. The examiner will select from the following:</td></tr>
<tr><td>C major</td><td>two octaves</td><td rowspan="3">min.
♩ = 88</td><td rowspan="3">scales separate bows
or slurred in pairs with a long tonic
(upper tonic may be repeated);
arpeggios separate bows only</td></tr>
<tr><td>D and G major</td><td>one octave</td></tr>
<tr><td>G minor
(scale only)</td><td>first 5 notes ascending
and descending</td></tr>
<tr><td colspan="4">Technical exercise (from memory) [♩ = 92]:</td></tr>
<tr><td colspan="4">Open strings</td></tr>
<tr><td colspan="4">or iii) Studies (music may be used):</td></tr>
<tr><td colspan="4">Candidates to prepare the following three studies. The candidate will choose one study to play first; the examiner will then select one of the remaining two studies to be performed.</td></tr>
<tr><td colspan="2">1. Back to Bach</td><td colspan="2">for tone and phrasing</td></tr>
<tr><td colspan="2">2. Nursery Slopes</td><td colspan="2">for mixed articulation and bowing styles</td></tr>
<tr><td colspan="2">3. The Sad Cowboy</td><td colspan="2">for cello techniques</td></tr>
</table>

i) Bowing exercise

Example: (♩ = 72)

ii) Scales, arpeggios & technical exercise

See pages 2-3 for bowing patterns.

C major scale (two octaves)

Grade 1 continued

C major arpeggio (two octaves)

D major scale (one octave)

D major arpeggio (one octave)

G major scale (one octave)

G major arpeggio (one octave)

G minor (to the 5th, scale only)

Technical exercise

Open strings:

iii) Studies

1. Back to Bach – tone and phrasing

2. Nursery Slopes – mixed articulation and bowing styles

3. The Sad Cowboy – cello techniques

Grade 2

Candidates to prepare i) Bowing exercise
i) Bowing exercise (from memory):
Candidates should play one of the Grade 2 scales, freely chosen from the list, with the rhythm ♩ ♫ on each degree of the scale, separate bows. The exercise may end with an additional long note on the tonic [♩ ♫ ♩]. [♩ = 80]

Candidates to prepare in full *either* section ii) *or* section iii)
either **ii) Scales, arpeggios & technical exercise** (from memory):
Candidates should play the scale and then the arpeggio. The examiner will select from the following:

C major	two octaves	min. tempi: scales: ♩ = 58 arpeggios: ♩. = 40	scales separate bows *or* slurred in pairs with a long tonic; arpeggios separate bows only
A, F and B♭ major	one octave		
G minor (candidate's choice of *either* natural *or* harmonic *or* melodic minor)			

Technical exercise (from memory) [♩ = 75-100]:
Fifths and sixths, starting on G, D *and* C strings
or **iii) Studies** (music may be used):
Candidates to prepare the following **three** studies. The candidate will choose one study to play first; the examiner will then select one of the remaining two studies to be performed.

1. Summer on the Swings	for tone and phrasing
2. When the Worm Met the Frog	for mixed articulation and bowing styles
3. A Change of Scene	for cello techniques

i) Bowing exercise

Example: (♩ = 80)

ii) Scales, arpeggios & technical exercise

See pages 2-3 for bowing patterns.

C major scale (two octaves)

C major arpeggio (two octaves)

A major scale (one octave)

A major arpeggio (one octave)

F major scale (one octave)

F major arpeggio (one octave)

B♭ major scale (one octave)

B♭ major arpeggio (one octave)

Grade 2 continued

G natural minor scale (one octave)

or

G harmonic minor scale (one octave)

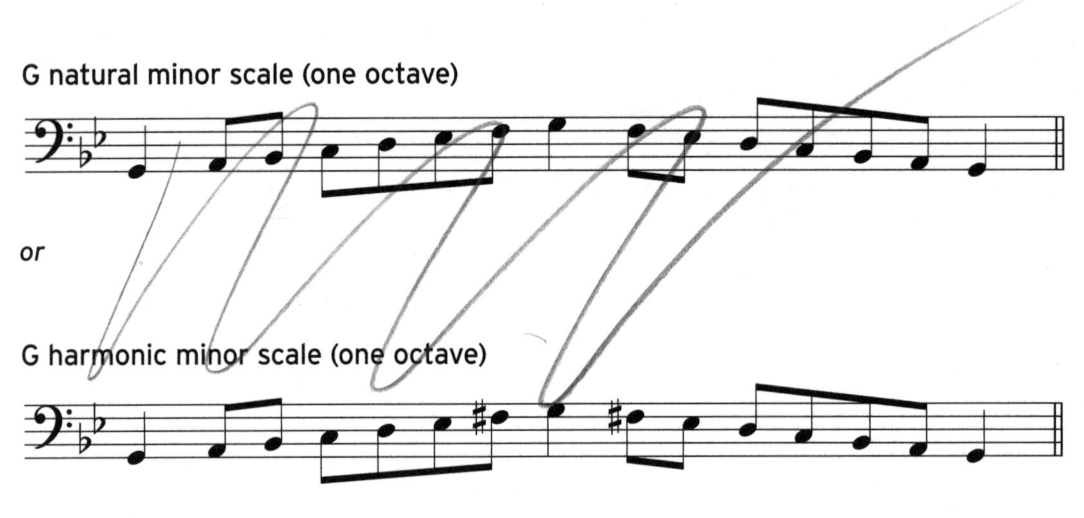

or

G melodic minor scale (one octave)

G minor arpeggio (one octave)

Technical exercise

Fifths and sixths

The following exercise to be performed in the pattern shown, starting on G, D *and* C strings:

(♩= 75-100)

iii) Studies

1. Summer on the Swings – tone and phrasing

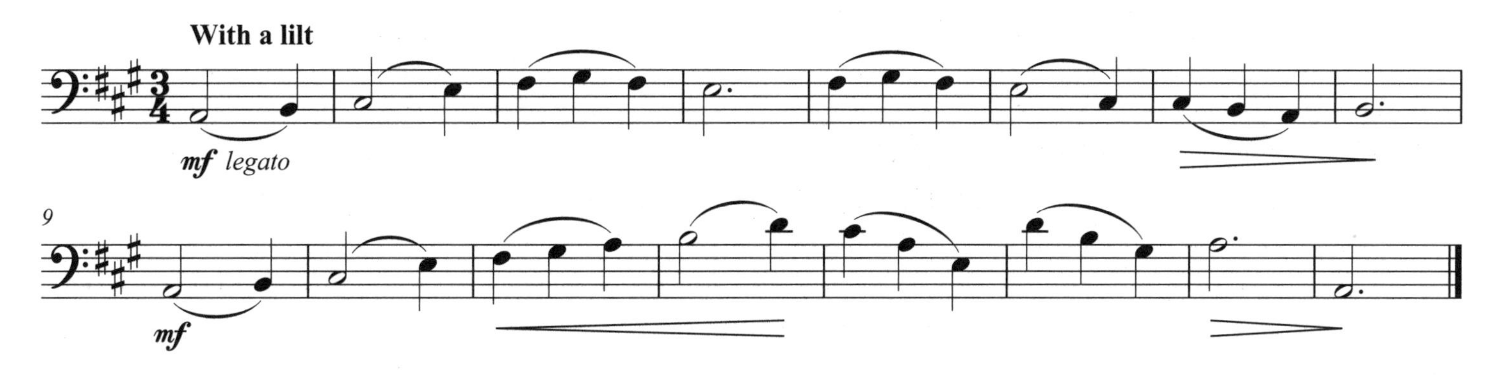

2. When the Worm Met the Frog – mixed articulation and bowing styles

3. A Change of Scene – cello techniques

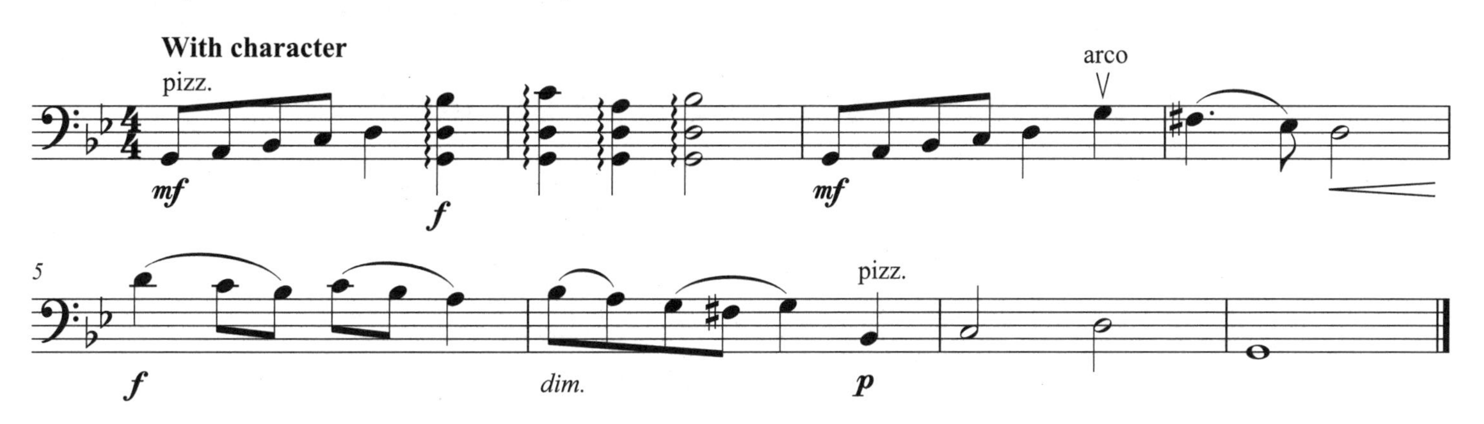

Grade 3

<table>
<tr><th colspan="6">Candidates to prepare i) Bowing exercise</th></tr>
<tr><td colspan="6">i) Bowing exercise (from memory):
Candidates should play one of the Grade 3 scales, freely chosen from the list, with four semiquavers on each degree of the scale. The exercise may end with an additional long note on the tonic. [♩ = 60]</td></tr>
<tr><th colspan="6">Candidates to prepare in full either section ii) or section iii)</th></tr>
<tr><td colspan="6">either ii) Scales, arpeggios & technical exercises (from memory):
Candidates should play the scale and then the arpeggio. The examiner will select from the following:</td></tr>
<tr><td>G major</td><td rowspan="2">two octaves</td><td rowspan="2"></td><td rowspan="6">min. tempi:
scales:
♩ = 60
arpeggios:
♩. = 40
7ths:
♩ = 60</td><td rowspan="4" colspan="2">scales separate bows or slurred in pairs with a long tonic;
arpeggios separate bows or slurred three notes to a bow</td></tr>
<tr><td>D and F major</td></tr>
<tr><td>E♭ major</td><td>one octave</td><td>starting on the C string</td></tr>
<tr><td>D minor
(candidate's choice of either harmonic or melodic minor)</td><td>two octaves</td><td></td></tr>
<tr><td>Dominant 7th in the key of C</td><td rowspan="2">one octave</td><td>starting on open G</td><td rowspan="2" colspan="2">separate bows
or slurred in pairs</td></tr>
<tr><td>Dominant 7th in the key of G</td><td>starting on 1st finger D on the C string</td></tr>
<tr><td colspan="6">Technical exercises (from memory):</td></tr>
<tr><td colspan="6">a) Chromatic phrase to be performed with separate bows [♩ = 60]
b) Fifths, sixths and octaves, starting on the open G, D and C strings [♩ = 76]</td></tr>
<tr><td colspan="6">or iii) Studies (music may be used):</td></tr>
<tr><td colspan="6">Candidates to prepare the following three studies. The candidate will choose one study to play first; the examiner will then select one of the remaining two studies to be performed.</td></tr>
<tr><td colspan="2">1. Take a Step Back</td><td colspan="4">for tone and phrasing</td></tr>
<tr><td colspan="2">2. Think of the Moments</td><td colspan="4">for mixed articulation and bowing styles</td></tr>
<tr><td colspan="2">3. Super Heroic</td><td colspan="4">for cello techniques</td></tr>
</table>

i) Bowing exercise

Example: (♩ = 60)

ii) Scales, arpeggios & technical exercises

See pages 2–3 for bowing patterns.

D major scale (two octaves)

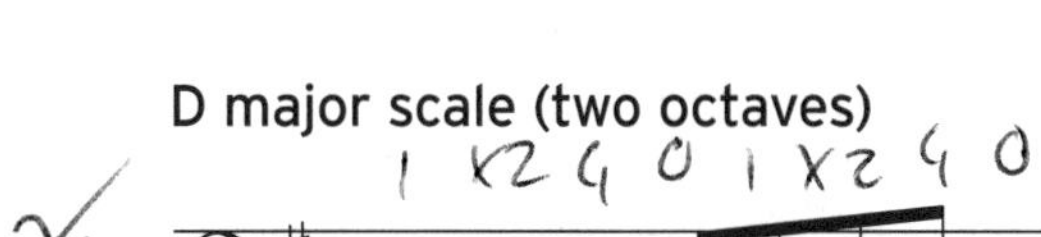

D major arpeggio (two octaves)

F major scale (two octaves)

F major arpeggio (two octaves)

E♭ major scale (one octave, starting on the C string)

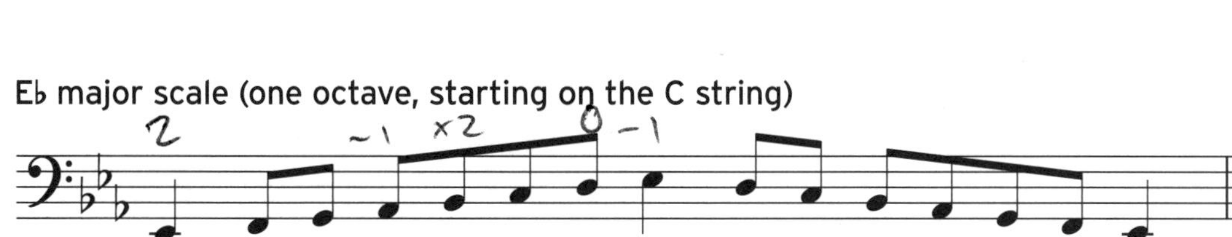

E♭ major arpeggio (one octave, starting on the C string)

D harmonic minor scale (two octaves)

or

D melodic minor scale (two octaves)

D minor arpeggio (two octaves)

Dominant 7th in the key of C (one octave, starting on open G)

Dominant 7th in the key of G (one octave, starting on 1st finger D on the C string)

Technical exercises

a) Chromatic phrase

to be performed with separate bows:

(♩= 60)

b) Fifths, sixths and octaves

The following exercise to be performed in the pattern shown starting on the open G, D *and* C strings:

iii) Studies

1. Take a Step Back – tone and phrasing

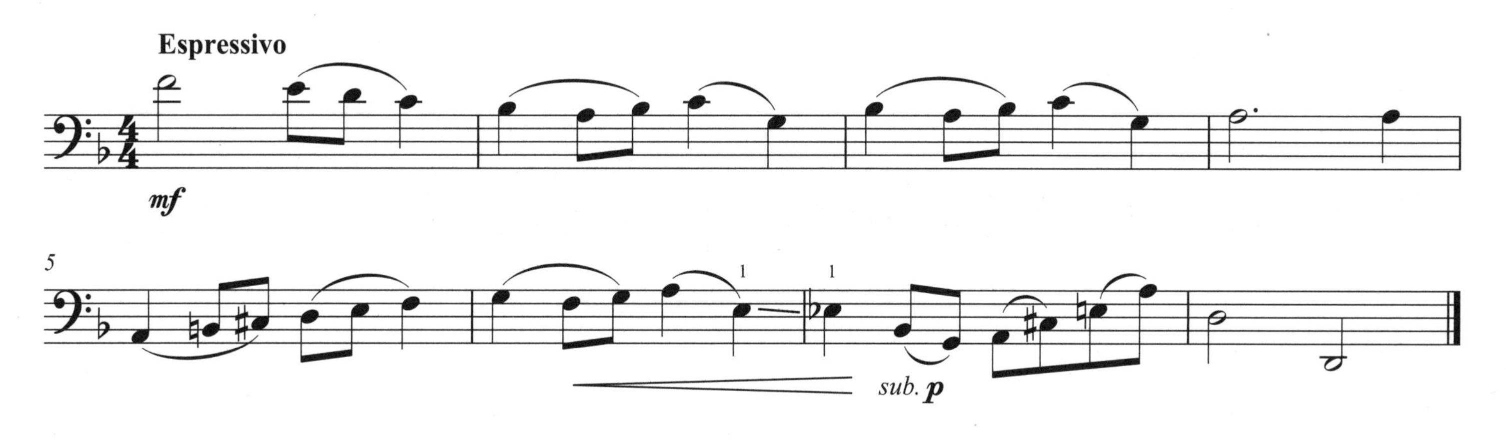

2. Think of the Moments – mixed articulation and bowing styles

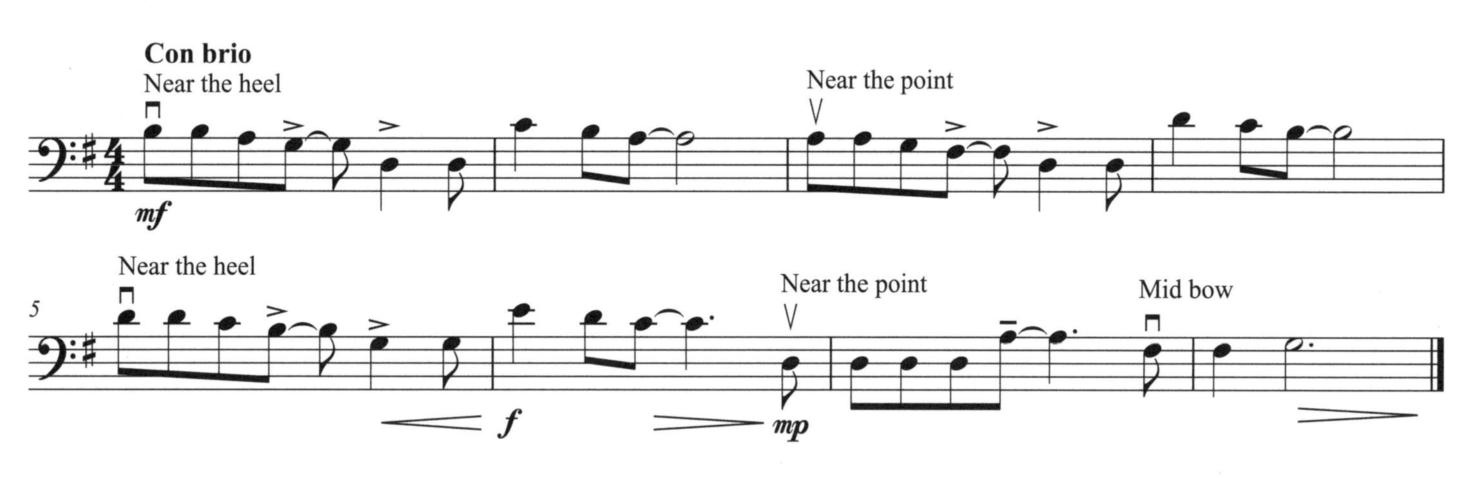

3. Super Heroic – cello techniques

Grade 4

Candidates to prepare i) Bowing exercise
i) Bowing exercise (from memory):
Candidates should play one of the Grade 4 scales, freely chosen from the list, with the rhythm ♪. ♬ on each degree of the scale. The exercise may end with an additional long note on the tonic. [♩. = 50]

Candidates to prepare in full *either* section ii) *or* section iii)
either **ii) Scales, arpeggios & technical exercise** (from memory):
Candidates should play the scale and then the arpeggio. The examiner will select from the following:

<table>
<tr><td>A, B♭ and E♭ major</td><td rowspan="4">two octaves</td><td rowspan="2"></td><td rowspan="6">min. tempi:
scales:
♩ = 69
arpeggios:
♩. = 44
7ths:
♩ = 69</td><td rowspan="2">scales separate bows or
slurred two crotchet beats to a bow;
arpeggios separate bows or
slurred three notes to a bow</td></tr>
<tr><td>C and G minor
(candidate's choice of either
harmonic or melodic minor)</td></tr>
<tr><td>Dominant 7th in the key of F</td><td>starting on open C</td><td rowspan="3">separate bows
or slurred in pairs</td></tr>
<tr><td>Dominant 7th in the key of G</td><td>starting on 1st finger D
on the C string</td></tr>
<tr><td>Dominant 7th in the key of E♭</td><td rowspan="2">one octave</td><td>starting on B♭</td></tr>
<tr><td>Chromatic scale</td><td>starting on open G</td><td>separate bows</td></tr>
</table>

Technical exercise (from memory) [♩ = 100]:
Octaves and sixths, starting on the open G, D *and* C strings
or **iii) Studies** (music may be used):
Candidates to prepare the following **three** studies. The candidate will choose one study to play first; the examiner will then select one of the remaining two studies to be performed.

1. Lament	for tone and phrasing
2. Countdown	for mixed articulation and bowing styles
3. Barcarolle	for cello techniques

i) Bowing exercise

Example: (♩. = 50)

ii) Scales, arpeggios & technical exercise

See pages 2–3 for bowing patterns.

A major scale (two octaves)

A major arpeggio (two octaves)

B♭ major scale (two octaves)

B♭ major arpeggio (two octaves)

E♭ major scale (two octaves)

E♭ major arpeggio (two octaves)

C harmonic minor scale (two octaves)

or

C melodic minor scale (two octaves)

C minor arpeggio (two octaves)

Grade 4 continued

G harmonic minor scale (two octaves)

or

G melodic minor scale (two octaves)

G minor arpeggio (two octaves)

Dominant 7th in the key of F (two octaves, starting on open C)

Dominant 7th in the key of G (two octaves, starting on 1st finger D on the C string)

Dominant 7th in the key of E♭ (one octave, starting on B♭)

Chromatic scale starting on open G (one octave)

Technical exercise

Octaves and sixths

The following exercise to be performed in the pattern shown, starting on the open G, D *and* C strings:

iii) Studies

1. Lament – tone and phrasing

2. Countdown – mixed articulation and bowing styles

Grade 4 continued

3. Barcarolle – cello techniques

Grade 5

Candidates to prepare i) Bowing exercise
i) Bowing exercise (from memory): Candidates should play one of the Grade 5 scales, freely chosen from the list, with a martelé bow stroke. [♩ = 88]

Candidates to prepare in full *either* section ii) *or* section iii)				
either **ii) Scales, arpeggios & technical exercises** (from memory): Candidates should play the scale and then the arpeggio. The examiner will select from the following:				
C major	three octaves		min. tempi: scales: ♩ = 69 arpeggios: ♩. = 44 7ths: ♩ = 69	scales separate bows *or* slurred two crotchet beats to a bow; arpeggios separate bows *or* slurred three notes to a bow
E and A♭ major	two octaves			
A and E minor (candidate's choice of *either* harmonic *or* melodic minor)				
D major scale	one octave	in thumb position starting on the D string		with a down and an up bow on each note
Chromatic scales starting on C and D	two octaves			separate bows *or* slurred four notes to a bow
Dominant 7th in the key of F		starting on C		
Dominant 7th in the key of G		starting on D		
Diminished 7th starting on A	one octave	starting on the G string, 1st finger		separate bows
Technical exercise (from memory) [♩ = 112]:				
Octaves, sixths and thirds, starting on the open G, D *and* C strings				
or **iii) Studies** (music may be used):				
Candidates to prepare the following **three** studies. The candidate will choose one study to play first; the examiner will then select one of the remaining two studies to be performed.				
1. Ornamental Journey	for tone and phrasing			
2. Tarantella	for mixed articulation and bowing styles			
3. On the Slide	for cello techniques			

i) Bowing exercise

Martelé: Immediately after the initial 'bite' or pressure accent (played between the middle and the point of the bow), the pressure must be released. The bow then moves quickly, but does not leave the string. Each stroke should end before applying pressure for the 'bite' at the start of the new stroke. This will result in an inevitable small silence between each note.

ii) Scales, arpeggios & technical exercise

See pages 2-3 for bowing patterns.

C major scale (three octaves)

Grade 5 continued

C major arpeggio (three octaves)

E major scale (two octaves)

E major arpeggio (two octaves)

A♭ major scale (two octaves)

A♭ major arpeggio (two octaves)

A harmonic minor scale (two octaves)

or

A melodic minor scale (two octaves)

A minor arpeggio (two octaves)

E harmonic minor scale (two octaves)

or

E melodic minor scale (two octaves)

E minor arpeggio (two octaves)

D major scale (one octave, in thumb position starting on the D string)

Chromatic scale starting on C (two octaves)

Chromatic scale starting on D (two octaves)

Grade 5 continued

Dominant 7th in the key of F (two octaves, starting on C)

Dominant 7th in the key of G (two octaves, starting on D)

Diminished 7th starting on A, 1st finger on the G string (one octave)

Technical exercise

Octaves, sixths and thirds

The following exercise to be performed in the pattern shown, starting on the open G, D *and* C strings:

iii) Studies

1. Ornamental Journey – tone and phrasing

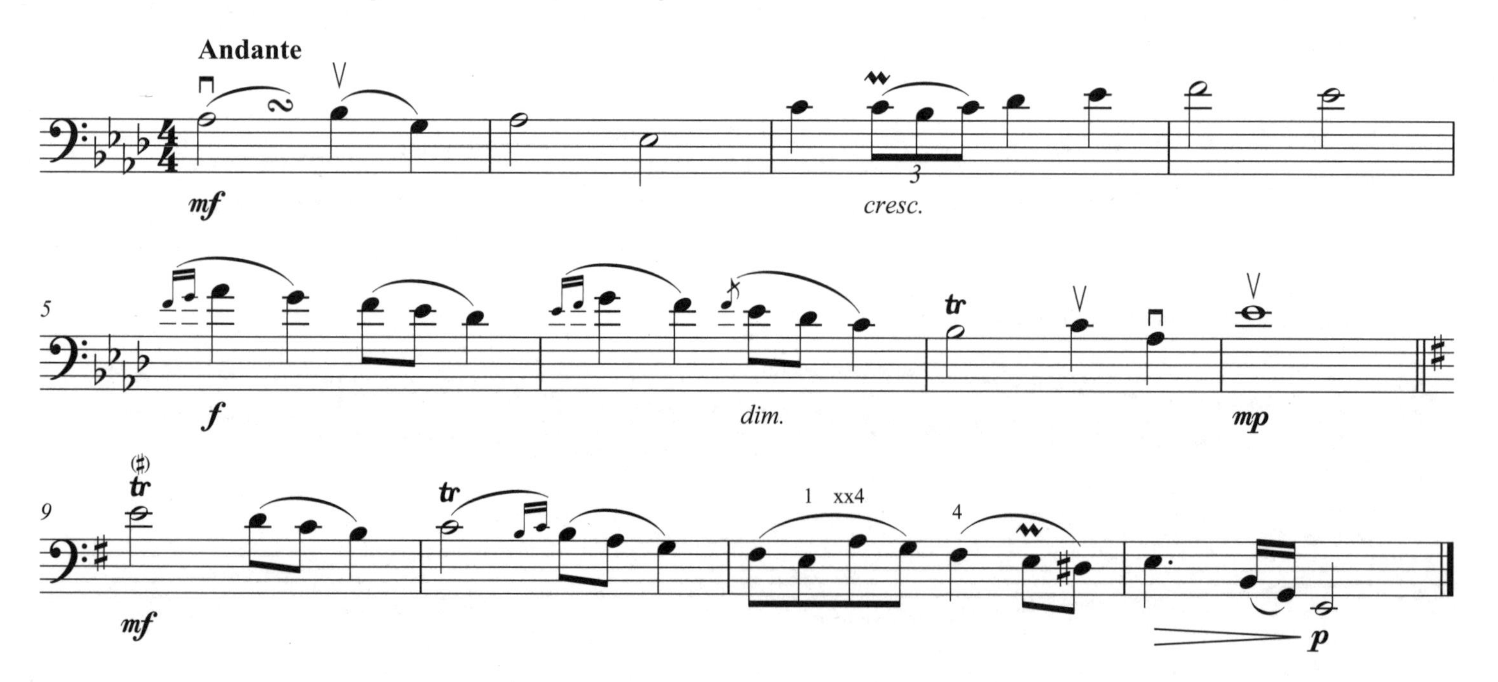

2. Tarantella – mixed articulation and bowing styles

3. On the Slide – cello techniques

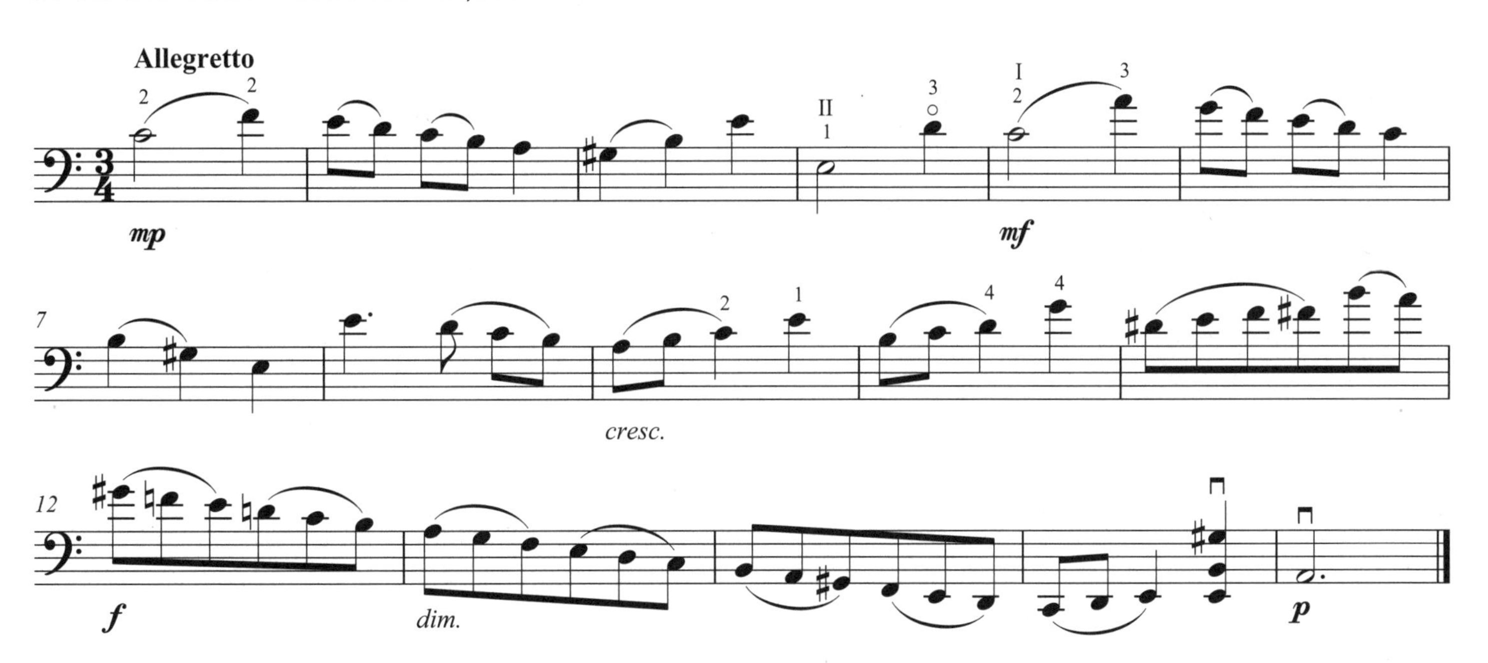

Grade 6

Candidates to prepare i) Bowing exercise

i) Bowing exercise (from memory):

Candidates should play one of the Grade 6 scales, freely chosen from the list, with each note of the scale played as two spiccato quavers. [♩ = 132]

Candidates to prepare in full *either* section ii) *or* section iii)

either **ii) Scales, arpeggios & technical exercise** (from memory):

Candidates should prepare major and minor scales and arpeggios from the following tonal centres, to be played with separate bows *or* slurred as requested by the examiner:

<table>
<tr><td>C</td><td>three octaves;
dominant 7th
two octaves</td><td rowspan="5">min. tempi:
scales:
♩ = 76
arpeggios:
♩. = 48
7ths:
♩ = 76</td><td rowspan="2">scales separate bows or slurred two crotchet beats to a bow;
arpeggios separate bows or slurred three notes to a bow</td></tr>
<tr><td>B and E♭</td><td>two octaves</td></tr>
<tr><td>Plus:
D major scale in thumb position, starting on the D string</td><td>one octave</td><td>separate bows or slurred in pairs with a long tonic</td></tr>
<tr><td>Chromatic scale starting on C♯ and E♭</td><td rowspan="2">two octaves</td><td rowspan="2">separate bows or slurred two crotchet beats to a bow</td></tr>
<tr><td>Diminished 7th starting on C and E</td></tr>
</table>

Major tonal centre

When the examiner requests a major tonal centre, the candidate should play in succession:

The major scale

The major arpeggio

The dominant 7th starting on that note and resolving onto the tonic
(to be prepared with separate bows and slurred two crotchet beats to a bow)

Minor tonal centre

When the examiner requests a minor tonal centre, the candidate should play in succession:

The melodic minor scale

The harmonic minor scale

The minor arpeggio

Technical exercise (from memory) [♩ = 100]:

Sixths in C major

or **iii) Orchestral extracts**

See current syllabus for details.

i) Bowing exercise

Spiccato: the bow should start off the string and leave the string after every note, creating a small 'saucer' or 'smile' shape over the string, and touching the string at the lowest point of the 'saucer' or 'smile' shape.

ii) Scales, arpeggios & technical exercise

See pages 2-3 for bowing patterns.

C major scale (three octaves) – see Grade 5, page 21

C major arpeggio (three octaves) – see Grade 5, page 22

Dominant 7th in the key of F, starting on C (two octaves) – see Grade 5, page 24

C melodic minor scale (three octaves)

C harmonic minor scale (three octaves)

C minor arpeggio (three octaves)

B major scale (two octaves)

Grade 6 continued

B major arpeggio (two octaves)

Dominant 7th in the key of E, starting on B (two octaves)

B melodic minor scale (two octaves)

B harmonic minor scale (two octaves)

B minor arpeggio (two octaves)

E♭ major scale (two octaves)

E♭ major arpeggio (two octaves)

Dominant 7th in the key of A♭, starting on E♭ (two octaves)

E♭ melodic minor scale (two octaves)

E♭ harmonic minor scale (two octaves)

E♭ minor arpeggio (two octaves)

D major scale in thumb position (one octave, starting on the D string)

Grade 6 continued

Chromatic scale starting on C♯ (two octaves)

Chromatic scale starting on E♭ (two octaves)

Diminished 7th starting on C (two octaves)

Diminished 7th starting on E (two octaves)

Technical exercise

Sixths in C major:

Grade 7

Candidates to prepare i) Bowing exercise

i) Bowing exercise (from memory):

Candidates should play one of the Grade 7 scales, freely chosen from the list, with hooked bowing. [♩ = 88]

Candidates to prepare in full *either* section ii) *or* section iii)

either **ii) Scales, arpeggios & technical exercises** (from memory):

Candidates should prepare major and minor scales and arpeggios from the following tonal centres, to be played with separate bows *or* slurred as requested by the examiner:

<table>
<tr><td>D, F and D♭/C♯</td><td>three octaves;
dominant 7ths
two octaves</td><td rowspan="4">min. tempi:
scales: ♩ = 84,
♩ = 100 (chromatic scales)
arpeggios:
♩. = 50
7ths:
♩ = 84</td><td>scales separate bows or slurred four crotchet beats to a bow;
arpeggios separate bows or slurred three notes to a bow</td></tr>
<tr><td>Plus:
Chromatic scales starting on E and D♭</td><td rowspan="2">two octaves</td><td>separate bows or slurred six notes to a bow</td></tr>
<tr><td>Diminished 7ths starting on F and F♯</td><td>separate bows or slurred two crotchet beats to a bow</td></tr>
<tr><td>Plus the following in thumb position:
D major scale and arpeggio
D melodic minor scale and arpeggio
D harmonic minor scale and arpeggio</td><td>one octave</td><td>scales separate bows or slurred two crotchet beats to a bow;
arpeggios separate bows or slurred three notes to a bow</td></tr>
</table>

Major tonal centre

When the examiner requests a major tonal centre, the candidate should play in succession:

The major scale

The major arpeggio

The dominant 7th starting on that note and resolving onto the tonic
(to be prepared with separate bows *and* slurred two crotchet beats to a bow)

Minor tonal centre

When the examiner requests a minor tonal centre, the candidate should play in succession:

The melodic minor scale

The harmonic minor scale

The minor arpeggio

Technical exercises (from memory) [♩ = 120]:

a) C major in sixths (one octave)

b) B♭ major in thirds (one octave)

or **iii) Orchestral extracts**

See current syllabus for details.

i) Bowing exercise

Hooked bowing: this describes a method of bowing a repeated dotted quaver-semiquaver rhythm. The bow should stop before each semiquaver, and the separation should be heard clearly.

Example: (♩ = 88)

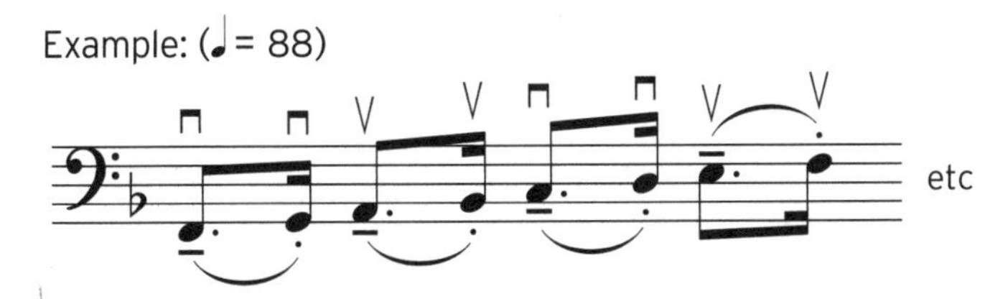

ii) Scales, arpeggios & technical exercises

See pages 2-3 for bowing patterns.

D major scale (three octaves)

D major arpeggio (three octaves)

Dominant 7th in the key of G, starting on D (two octaves) – see Grade 5, page 24

D melodic minor scale (three octaves)

D harmonic minor scale (three octaves)

D minor arpeggio (three octaves)

F major scale (three octaves)

F major arpeggio (three octaves)

Dominant 7th in the key of B♭, starting on F (two octaves)

F melodic minor scale (three octaves)

Grade 7 continued

F harmonic minor scale (three octaves)

F minor arpeggio (three octaves)

D♭/C♯ major scale (three octaves)

D♭/C♯ major arpeggio (three octaves)

Dominant 7th in the key of G♭, starting on D♭ (two octaves)

C♯/D♭ melodic minor scale (three octaves)

C♯/D♭ harmonic minor scale (three octaves)

C♯/D♭ minor arpeggio (three octaves)

Chromatic scale starting on E (two octaves)

Grade 7 continued

Chromatic scale starting on D♭ (two octaves)

Diminished 7th starting on F (two octaves)

Diminished 7th starting on F♯ (two octaves)

D major scale in thumb position (one octave)

D major arpeggio in thumb position (one octave)

D melodic minor scale in thumb position (one octave)

D harmonic minor scale in thumb position (one octave)

D minor arpeggio in thumb position (one octave)

Technical exercises

a) C major in sixths (one octave, in the following pattern):

b) B♭ major in thirds (one octave):

Grade 8

<table>
<tr><th colspan="4">Candidates to prepare i) Bowing exercise</th></tr>
<tr><td colspan="4">i) Bowing exercise (from memory):
Candidates should choose one of the Grade 8 scales, and the examiner will choose any one of the specified bowings from Grades 5-7 and ask the candidate to play the scale with that bowing.</td></tr>
<tr><th colspan="4">Candidates to prepare in full either section ii) or section iii)</th></tr>
<tr><td colspan="4">either ii) Scales, arpeggios & technical exercises (from memory):
Candidates should prepare major and minor scales and arpeggios from the following tonal centres, to be played with separate bows or slurred as requested by the examiner:</td></tr>
<tr><td>A, F♯, B♭ and D♭/C♯</td><td>three octaves; dominant 7ths two octaves</td><td rowspan="3">min. tempi:
scales:
♩ = 92,
♩ = 100
(chromatic scales)
arpeggios:
♩. = 50
7ths:
♩ = 92</td><td>scales separate bows or slurred four crotchet beats to a bow;
arpeggios separate bows or slurred three notes to a bow</td></tr>
<tr><td>Plus:
Chromatic scales starting on A, F♯, B♭ and D♭</td><td rowspan="2">two octaves</td><td>separate bows or slurred twelve notes to a bow</td></tr>
<tr><td>Diminished 7ths starting on
A, F♯, B♭ and C♯</td><td>separate bows or slurred two crotchet beats to a bow</td></tr>
<tr><td colspan="4">Major tonal centre
When the examiner requests a major tonal centre, the candidate should play in succession:
The major scale
The major arpeggio
The dominant 7th starting on that note and resolving onto the tonic
(to be prepared with separate bows and slurred two crotchet beats to a bow)
Minor tonal centre
When the examiner requests a minor tonal centre, the candidate should play in succession:
The melodic minor scale
The harmonic minor scale
The minor arpeggio</td></tr>
<tr><td colspan="4">Technical exercises (from memory) [♩ = 120]:</td></tr>
<tr><td colspan="4">a) E♭ major in thirds (one octave)
b) C major in sixths (one octave)
c) G major in octaves (one octave)</td></tr>
<tr><td colspan="4">or iii) Orchestral extracts</td></tr>
<tr><td colspan="4">See current syllabus for details.</td></tr>
</table>

i) Bowing exercise

See Grades 5-7.

ii) Scales, arpeggios & technical exercises

See pages 2–3 for bowing patterns.

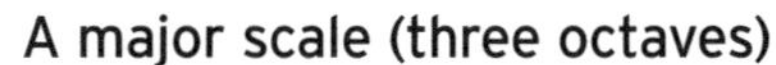
A major scale (three octaves)

A major arpeggio (three octaves)

Dominant 7th in the key of D, starting on A (two octaves)

A melodic minor scale (three octaves)

A harmonic minor scale (three octaves)

Grade 8 continued

A minor arpeggio (three octaves)

F♯ major scale (three octaves)

F♯ major arpeggio (three octaves)

Dominant 7th in the key of B, starting on F♯ (two octaves)

F♯ melodic minor scale (three octaves)

F♯ harmonic minor scale (three octaves)

F♯ minor arpeggio (three octaves)

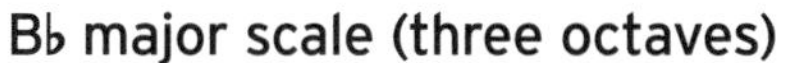

B♭ major scale (three octaves)

B♭ major arpeggio (three octaves)

Dominant 7th in the key of E♭, starting on B♭ (two octaves)

Grade 8 continued

Bb melodic minor scale (three octaves)

Bb harmonic minor scale (three octaves)

Bb minor arpeggio (three octaves)

Db/C# tonal centre – see Grade 7, pages 34-35

Chromatic scale starting on A (two octaves)

Chromatic scale starting on F♯ (two octaves)

Chromatic scale starting on B♭ (two octaves)

Chromatic scale starting on D♭ (two octaves) – see Grade 7, page 36

Diminished 7th starting on A (two octaves)

Diminished 7th starting on F♯ (two octaves) – see Grade 7, page 36

Diminished 7th starting on B♭ (two octaves)

Diminished 7th starting on C♯ (two octaves)

Grade 8 continued

Technical exercises

a) E♭ major in thirds (one octave):

b) C major in sixths (one octave):

c) G major in octaves (one octave):